This prayer journal is dedicated to all Recruits, Coasties, parents, grandparents, aunts, uncles, spouses, and all other loved ones who have and are going on this journey with them and have shown love and support through prayer. To the Coasties and Vets thank you for your service. We hope that this prayer journal is helpful and serves as a guide during times of first good-byes, training, deployments, and the everyday sacrifice that our Coasties and families endure by keeping our country safe.

God Bless you all.

Be•Inspired
A subsidiary of:
Two Girls and a Reading Corner
© 2021 Mandy Leigh
ISBN: 978-1-952879-31-9

Two Girls and a Reading Corner
PO Box 2404, Madison, Al 35758

The Coast Guard Prayer

Almighty and Everlasting God,
Whose hand stills the tumult of the deep,
we offer our prayers for those who serve in
our Coast Guard. We are mindful of their
traditions of selfless service to the seafarers
who make their ways to appointed ports.
Employ their devotions of good ends as they
track the weather and search for the seas for
those in extremity of storm, shipwreck or
battle. Make their soundings and markings
sure that safe passages may be found by those
who go down to the sea in ships. Encourage
them, O Lord, as they stand guard over our
coasts and the bulwarks of our freedoms.
Graciously deliver them from threatening
calamities in all their perilous voyages. Bless
the keepers of the lights and be Thou their
close friend in lonely watches. Keep the
beacons of honor and duty burning that they
may reach the home port with duty well
performed, in service to Thee and our land.

AMEN.

30 Day Prayer Challenge

Prayer is the Native Language of Faith.

Prayer list

What I'm Grateful For...

FAVORITE SCRIPTURES & QUOTES

MY NOTES

THOUGHTS & NOTES

Answered Prayers

30 Day Prayer Challenge

Prayer is the Native Language of Faith.

Prayer list

What I'm Grateful For...

FAVORITE SCRIPTURES & QUOTES

MY NOTES

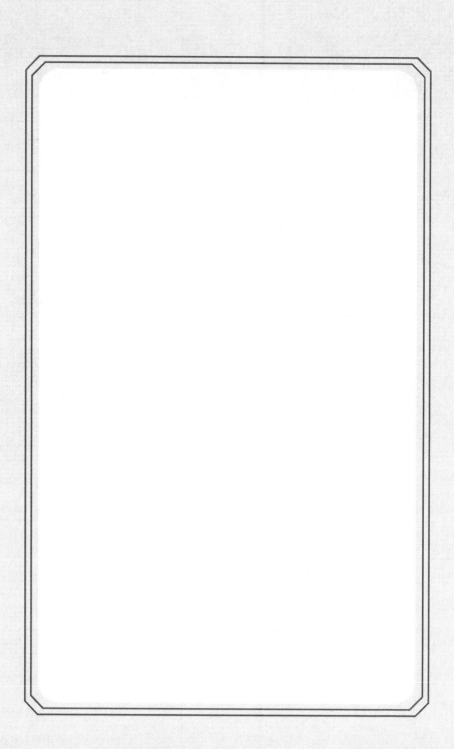

THOUGHTS & NOTES

Answered Prayers

30 Day Prayer Challenge

Prayer is the Native Language of Faith.

Prayer list

What I'm Grateful For...

FAVORITE SCRIPTURES & QUOTES

MY NOTES

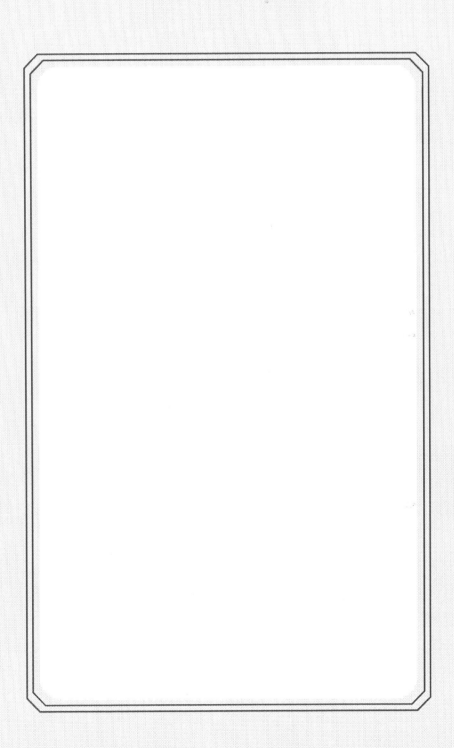

THOUGHTS & NOTES

30 Day Prayer Challenge

Prayer is the Native Language of Faith.

Prayer list

What I'm Grateful For...

FAVORITE SCRIPTURES & QUOTES

MY NOTES

THOUGHTS & NOTES

30 Day Prayer Challenge

Prayer is the Native Language of Faith.

Prayer list

What I'm Grateful For...

FAVORITE SCRIPTURES & QUOTES

MY NOTES

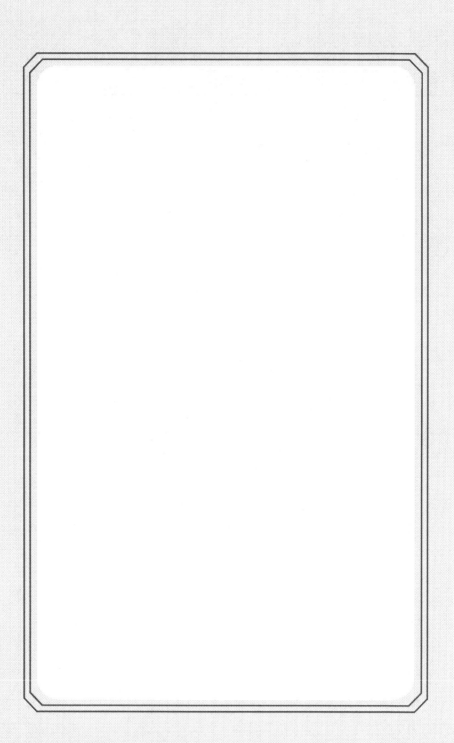

THOUGHTS & NOTES

Answered Prayers

30 Day Prayer Challenge

Prayer is the Native Language of Faith.

Prayer list

What I'm Grateful For...

FAVORITE SCRIPTURES & QUOTES

MY NOTES

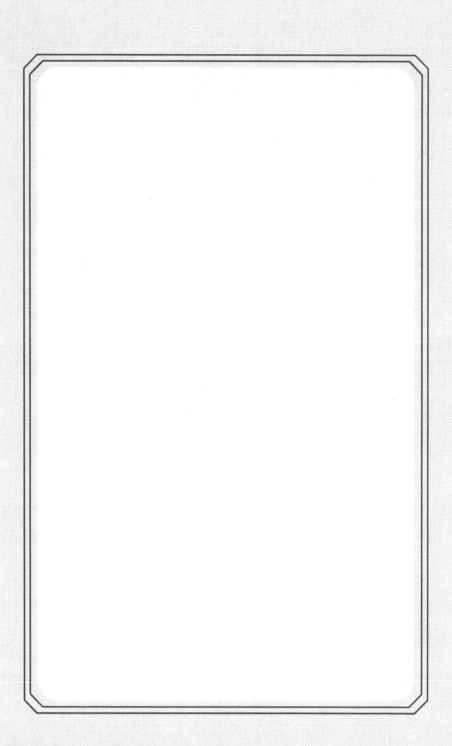

THOUGHTS & NOTES

30 Day Prayer Challenge

Prayer is the Native Language of Faith.

Prayer list

What I'm Grateful For...

FAVORITE SCRIPTURES & QUOTES

MY NOTES

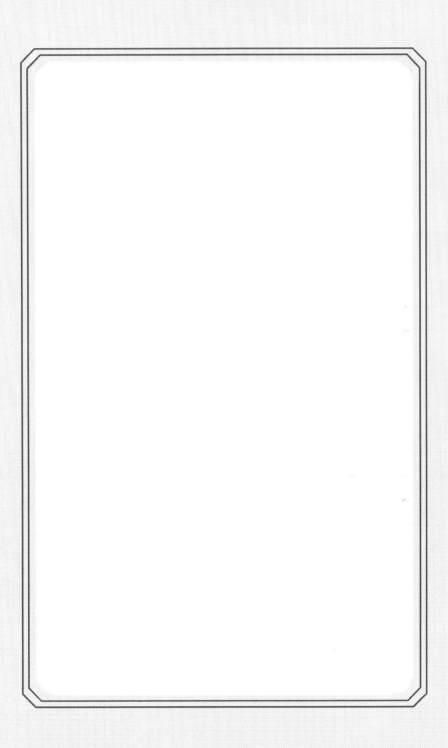

THOUGHTS & NOTES

Answered Prayers

30 Day Prayer Challenge

Prayer is the Native Language of Faith.

Prayer list

What I'm Grateful For...

FAVORITE SCRIPTURES & QUOTES

MY NOTES

THOUGHTS & NOTES

Answered Prayers

30 Day Prayer Challenge

Prayer is the Native Language of Faith.

Prayer list

What I'm Grateful For...

FAVORITE SCRIPTURES & QUOTES

MY NOTES

THOUGHTS & NOTES

30 Day Prayer Challenge

Prayer is the Native Language of Faith.

Prayer list

What I'm Grateful For...

FAVORITE SCRIPTURES & QUOTES

MY NOTES

THOUGHTS & NOTES

30 Day Prayer Challenge

Prayer is the Native Language of Faith.

Prayer list

What I'm Grateful For...

FAVORITE SCRIPTURES & QUOTES

MY NOTES

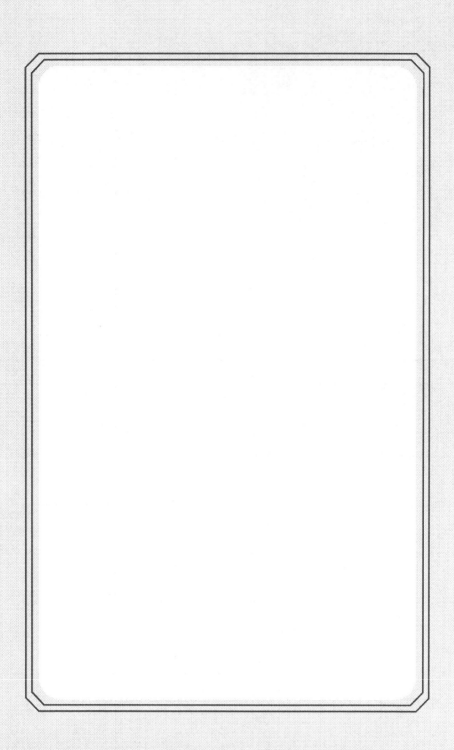

THOUGHTS & NOTES

Answered Prayers

30 Day Prayer Challenge

Prayer is the Native Language of Faith.

Prayer list

What I'm Grateful For...

FAVORITE SCRIPTURES & QUOTES

MY NOTES

THOUGHTS & NOTES

Answered Prayers

Made in the USA
Middletown, DE
13 May 2024

54304061R00205